EXPLORING MATHEMATICS ON YOUR OWN

Topology

EXPLORING MATHEMATICS ON YOUR OWN

Topology
THE RUBBER-SHEET GEOMETRY

DONOVAN A. JOHNSON

WILLIAM H. GLENN

JOHN MURRAY
London

The Strange World
of Topology

What Is Topology?

Have you ever heard of a sheet of paper with only one side? Why do mathematicians say that a doughnut and a flowerpot are more alike than a doughnut and a chestnut? When is a triangle the same as a circle? Is it possible to change a left shoe to a right shoe by taking a trip around space? These are the kinds of questions that topology answers. This doesn't sound very much like mathematics, does it? But it is, and it's one of the newest and most exciting fields of mathematics. Since it talks about things that are familiar to you, like the inside of a glove or the difference between right and left shoes, it will not be too strange for you. And topology is so full of impossibilities, tricks, and puzzles that it will be fun to learn more about it.

Topology is the branch of mathematics that decides what is possible. It tells us whether it is possible to turn an inner tube inside out. You may think this is an easy problem. Topologists say it is possible, but no one has ever been able to do it with a real inner tube.

In topology, we never ask, "How long?", "How far?", or "How big?" Instead, we ask, "Where?", "Between what?", "Inside or outside?" A traveller on a strange road would not ask, "How far is Barchester?" if he did not know the direction. The answer, "Three miles from here," would not help him very much if there were several roads. He is more likely to ask, "How do I get to Barchester?" Then the answer, "Follow this road until you come to a fork, then turn to your left," will tell him how to get to Barchester. This answer does not sound mathematical because it says nothing about distances and does not describe whether the path is straight or curved. This is the kind of answer that topology gives to questions.

Topology and Geometry

Topology is something like geometry because it deals with lines, points, and figures. But the figures are different from those of geometry because they are permitted to change in size and shape. So, someone has called it "rubber-sheet geometry." Topology is more interested in position than in size or shape. It deals with the properties of position that are not affected by changes in size and shape. For example, suppose you draw a square on a rubber sheet, with a dot inside the square. No matter how you stretch the rubber sheet, the dot will always be on the inside of the square. So topology is the study of geometrical properties that stay the same in spite of stretching or bending.

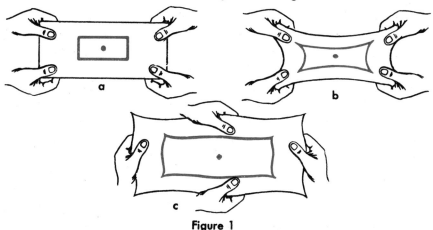

Figure 1

Distance has no meaning in topology. Two points an inch apart may easily be made two inches apart by stretching. Likewise, angle size is meaningless because you can stretch a rubber sheet so that an angle of 15° becomes an angle of 35°. Even straight lines have no meaning in topology because the straight line AB

$$A \text{ ———————————— } B$$

Figure 2

3

may become a curved line by stretching the sheet:

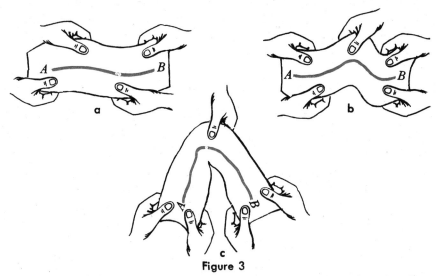

Figure 3

The straight line not only becomes a curved line, but it also changes in length.

We usually think of an object like a key as hard and rigid. It keeps its shape and fits the lock for years and years, no matter how much it has been moved about. When an aeroplane takes off and flies away it seems to become smaller. But we know it stays the same size no matter where it is. Euclidean geometry is the study of objects which always stay the same size. Topology is the study of things which do change in size and shape when moved. It starts with the idea that there are no rigid bodies; everything can change in size, shape, and position.

We can think of a line as being like a piece of string. If a point is on a line, like a knot on a string, it must remain on that line even though the line is twisted, stretched, or curved in many ways. We also say that a line is *continuous*. There are no holes in the line. Whenever a line crosses another line, it passes through a point on that line. This means, for example, that if you draw a line *CD* through line *XY*, as in the figure below, line *CD* passes through a point on line *XY*.

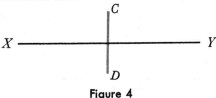

Figure 4

So many of the properties of lines and figures change in this rubber-sheet geometry that you may think nothing remains the same. This is not true. Look at the line AB in Figure 2 again. No matter how we stretch or bend the sheet, the path from A to B remains a path from A to B which does not cross itself. The line or path may become crooked, or longer, even more than in Figure 3, but it remains a line or path from A to B. In topology, a path or line like AB is called *Arc AB*.

How Geometrical Figures Change in Topology

What we have said about simple lines like AB also applies to lines that form geometrical figures such as circles or triangles.

Let us see what happens to a circle on a rubber sheet. By stretching the sheet, the circle may change as pictured below.

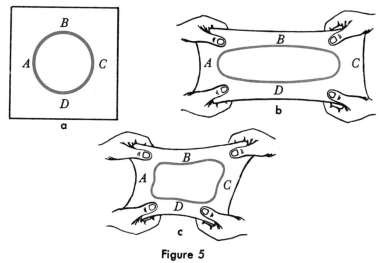

Figure 5

We can see that the circle changes a great deal in shape and size. But no matter how we stretch the sheet, the figure remains a path, $ABCDA$. We can also see that no matter where we start on this path, we will return to the starting point without crossing the path. If we start at C, we will pass through B, A, D and return to C. In topology, all these figures have the same name. Each is called a *simple closed curve* or a *closed circuit*. Each is made up of the two arcs ABC and ADC which have only the points A and C in common.

5

Look at the geometrical figures below:

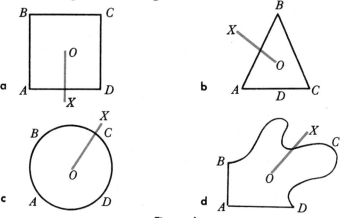

Figure 6

Topology says these figures are all simple closed curves. Each one is made up of two arcs, *ABC* and *ADC*. It doesn't make any difference whether the arcs are straight or curved.

In each illustration above, there is a point *O* inside the closed curve and a point *X* outside the closed curve. The line *OX* crosses an arc of the closed curve. No matter how these figures may be changed by stretching, *OX* will always cross an arc of the curve. The closed arc *ABCDA* has no holes in it for *OX* to sneak through.

This idea of no holes in a line sounds simple, but it is a very important idea. We have seen that this idea of no holes in a line is called *continuity*. Actually, nobody knows whether a line has a hole or not. But it seems sensible to assume that there are no holes in a line.

We say that these closed curves divide the sheet into two parts, an *inside* and an *outside*. You cannot go from the inside to the outside without crossing the closed curve. This holds true no matter how you change the shape. Since you always cross the line in going from the outside to the inside no matter how you distort the figure, we call this crossing an *invariant* situation. Any situation in topology that stays the same under distortion is called an *invariant*. When we distort a figure — for example, a straight line stretched into a curved line or a square into a circle — we have made a change called a *topological change* or *topological transformation*. These transformations change the size or shape of the figure but do not form a new topological figure. If we cut, tear, or fold a line or a surface, we change the

6

line or surface so that it has new features. So a topological transformation is made *without* cutting, tearing, folding, or punching
holes.

In the circle *ABCD*, another property which does not change,
or is invariant, is the order of the points *A*, *B*, *C*, *D*. What was
invariant about the line *AB*? No matter how it was stretched,
it remained a path from *A* to *B* without crossing itself. We have
seen that in topology a circle may change into an ellipse or a
square and a straight line may become a curved line. But when
we join points *A* and *B* of the line *AB*, as in Figure 7, we have a
new figure, a closed curve.

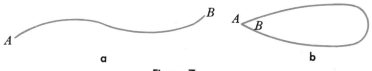

Figure 7

In a similar way, when we cut the arc of a circle, as in Figure
8, we change the closed curve to a line.

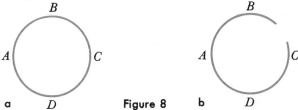

Figure 8

These changes are *not* transformations. New topological figures
are formed.

In geometry, we study the properties of size, shape, area, and
angle size. We say figures are congruent when we can place one
figure upon another of the same shape and size with all parts
matching. Topological transformations give figures that are said
to be *equivalent*. In topology, the circle and square are equivalent
no matter how they differ in size. Both of them have one inside
and one outside. To go from the inside to the outside, we must
cross one line. If we shade the inside of the figure below we can
easily see how it divides the surface of the picture into two regions.

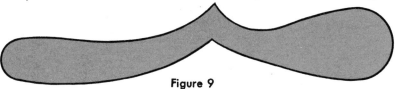

Figure 9

The idea of an inside and an outside helps solve interesting problems, like the old story about a Persian Caliph who used a topology problem to select a husband for his beautiful daughter. She had so many suitors that he decided to pick the one who was best at solving problems. The first problem given to the suitors

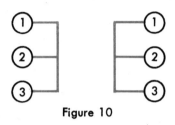

Figure 10

is illustrated in Figure 10. The problem was to connect like numbers by lines that did not cross each other or any other lines in the figure. Any suitor who solved this problem successfully could then talk to the Caliph's daughter.

This was an easy problem and made all the suitors excited. See if you can solve this problem. Would you have been permitted to talk to the Caliph's daughter?

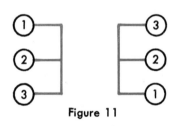

Figure 11

But the one who could marry the Caliph's daughter had to solve a second problem. The second problem was again to connect like numbers with lines that did not cross each other or any other lines. But note how the drawing has changed. Can you solve this problem?

Someone has said the Caliph's daughter died an old maid. What do you think?

A solution for the first problem looks like this.

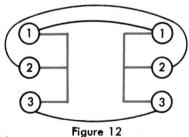

Figure 12

That was easy!

For the second problem, let's draw lines from 1 to 1, and 2 to 2. Now we have a simple closed curve. The inside is shaded.

One 3 is inside the closed curve, and the other 3 is outside. And we know that you can't get from the inside to the outside of a simple closed curve without crossing a line; so topology says it is impossible to draw the lines without crossing.

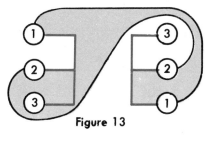

Figure 13

In the Caliph's problem, we worked with a simple closed curve having one inside and one outside. Topology is also concerned with other curves that are not simple closed curves. Closed figures like the one below have more than one inside. Do you see five regions (four inside areas) in Figure 14?

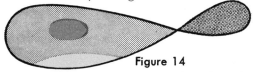

Figure 14

Now look at Figure 15. In each drawing, into how many regions is the sheet divided? How many inside regions does each one have?

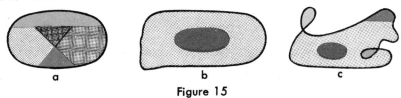

Figure 15

EXERCISE SET 1
Topological Curves and Regions

1. Which of the following figures are topological lines?

2. Which of the following figures are simple closed curves?

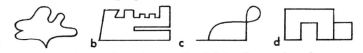

3. How many inside regions does each of these figures have?

9

Fun with the Moebius Strip

All the closed surfaces we have talked about have been on the surface of a sheet. All the sheets we know of, like a sheet of paper, have two surfaces: a front and a back. Have you ever seen a piece of paper with only one surface? There really is such a sheet. It is called a *Moebius strip* and has been used by many magicians to entertain people. It has been a plaything for mathematicians ever since it was discovered by August Ferdinand Moebius, a German mathematician, in 1858. A fly can walk from any point on this strip to any other point without crossing an edge. Unlike a sheet of paper or a table top, it does not have a top or a bottom, or a front or a back.

You can make a Moebius strip with any strip of paper. Any size or type of paper will do, but gummed tape an inch or two wide and one or two feet long is easy to handle. We use the strip to make a ring or band. But before we glue the ends together, we give one end a half-twist. If you use gummed tape, twist one end so that you stick the gummed side of one end to the gummed side of the other end. Attach the band as illustrated in Figure 16.

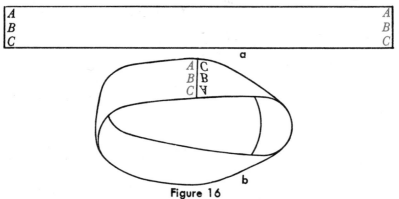

Figure 16

If you draw a line on the surface of your Moebius strip, you will find that you will go all around the entire surface without crossing an edge. Paint or colour one surface without going over an edge. Is there another surface that remains to be coloured?

For another unusual result, cut the band lengthwise along a line in the centre of the strip. What unexpected result did you obtain? If you make another band, and cut it lengthwise one third of the way in from an edge, you will obtain yet a different result.

If you put the Caliph's problem that we discussed on page 8 on a Moebius strip, you should be able to win the Caliph's daughter. Try it. In doing this, be sure to draw your lines all the way around the strip, in the same way that you painted the strip.

The Moebius strip enables us to take a new look at right- and left-handed objects like shoes or gloves. If you compare the two gloves of a pair of gloves, you will find that they are equal in all measurements you can make. But you know the gloves are very different. The left-handed glove won't fit your right hand.

How can you change a right-handed glove to a left-handed one? In two dimensions it seems possible on a Moebius strip. If you could slide a picture of the glove along the surface of a Moebius strip, the glove would be upside down and backward when it got back to the starting point.

EXERCISE SET 2
Moebius Strip Facts

You can have fun showing your friends the odd results you get by cutting Moebius strips in different ways. Copy and complete the table below to see what happens when you change the number of twists and the way in which you cut the strip.

Number of Half-Twists	Number of Sides and Edges	Kind of Cut	Results of Cut (Number of sides and edges, length and width, number of loops, twists, and knots)
0		centre	
1		centre	
1		one-third	
2		centre	
2		one-third	
3		centre	
3		one-third	

Here's a story about the legendary Paul Bunyan that shows how the Moebius strip has some "practical" applications.

Paul Bunyan versus the Conveyor Belt

By William Hazlett Upson*

One of Paul Bunyan's most brilliant successes came about not because of brilliant thinking, but because of Paul's caution and carefulness. This was the famous affair of the conveyor belt.

Paul and his mechanic, Ford Fordsen, had started to work a uranium mine in Colorado. The ore was brought out on an endless belt which ran half a mile going into the mine and another half mile coming out — giving it a total length of one mile. It was four feet wide. It ran on a series of rollers, and was driven by a pulley mounted on the transmission of Paul's big blue truck "Babe." The manufacturers of the belt had made it all in one piece, without any splice or lacing, and they had put a half-twist in the return part so that the wear would be the same on both sides.

After several months' operation, the mine gallery had become twice as long, but the amount of material coming out was less. Paul decided he needed a belt twice as long and half as wide. He told Ford Fordsen to take his chain saw and cut the belt in two lengthwise.

"That will give us two belts," said Ford Fordsen. "We'll have to cut them in two crosswise and splice them together. That means I'll have to go to town and buy the materials for two splices."

"No," said Paul. "This belt has a half-twist — which makes it what is known in geometry as a Moebius strip."

"What difference does that make?" asked Ford Fordsen.

"A Moebius strip," said Paul Bunyan, "has only one side, and one edge, and if we cut it in two lengthwise, it will still be in one piece. We'll have one belt twice as long and half as wide."

"How can you cut something in two and have it still in one piece?" asked Ford Fordsen.

Paul was modest. He was never opinionated. "Let's try this thing out," he said.

They went into Paul's office. Paul took a strip of gummed paper about two inches wide and a yard long. He laid it on his desk with the gummed side up. He lifted the two ends and brought them together in front of him with the gummed sides down. Then he turned one of the ends over, licked it, slid it under the other end, and stuck the two

*Reprinted from the *Ford Times*, by permission of the Ford Motor Company.

12

gummed sides together. He had made himself an endless paper belt with a half-twist in it just like the big belt on the conveyor.

"This," said Paul, "is a Moebius strip. It will perform just the way I said — I hope."

Paul took a pair of scissors, dug the point in the centre of the paper and cut the paper strip in two lengthwise. And when he had finished — sure enough — he had one strip twice as long, half as wide, and with a double twist in it.

Ford Fordsen was convinced. He went out and started cutting the big belt in two. And, at this point, a man called Loud Mouth Johnson arrived to see how Paul's enterprise was coming along, and to offer any destructive criticism that might occur to him. Loud Mouth Johnson, being Public Blow-Hard Number One, found plenty to find fault with.

"If you cut that belt in two lengthwise, you will end up with two belts, each the same length as the original belt, but only half as wide."

"No," said Ford Fordsen, "this is a very special belt known as a Moebius strip. If I cut it in two lengthwise, I will end up with one belt twice as long and half as wide."

"Want to bet?" said Loud Mouth Johnson.

"Sure," said Ford Fordsen.

They bet a thousand dollars. And, of course, Ford Fordsen won. Loud Mouth Johnson was so astounded that he slunk off and stayed away for six months. When he finally came back he found Paul Bunyan just starting to cut the belt in two lengthwise for the second time.

"What's the idea?" asked Loud Mouth Johnson.

Paul Bunyan said, "The tunnel has progressed much farther and the material coming out is not as bulky as it was. So I am lengthening the belt again and making it narrower."

"Where is Ford Fordsen?"

Paul Bunyan said, "I have sent him to town to get some materials to splice the belt. When I get through cutting it in two lengthwise I will have two belts of the same length but only half the width of this one. So I will have to do some splicing."

Loud Mouth Johnson could hardly believe his ears. Here was a chance to get his thousand dollars back and show up Paul Bunyan as a boob besides. "Listen," said Loud Mouth Johnson, "when you get through you will have only one belt twice as long and half as wide."

"Want to bet?"

"Sure."

So they bet a thousand dollars and, of course, Loud Mouth Johnson lost again. It wasn't so much that Paul Bunyan was brilliant. It was just that he was methodical. He had tried it out with that strip of gummed paper, and he knew that the second time you slice a Moebius strip you get two pieces — linked together like an old fashioned watch chain.

Topology Solves
Some Interesting Problems

A Bridge Problem and Topology

In the eighteenth century, in the sleepy German university town of Koenigsberg (now the Russian city of Kaliningrad), Sunday strollers were fond of ambling along the banks of the Preger River, which meandered through the town and was crossed by seven bridges. These bridges ran from each bank of the river to two islands in the river, with one bridge joining the islands, as shown in this drawing.

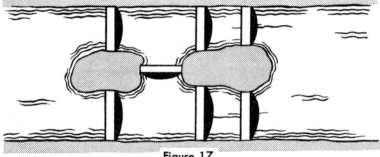

Figure 17

One day, a native asked his neighbour this question: "How can you take a Sunday stroll so that you cross each of our seven bridges and cross each bridge exactly once?" The problem intrigued the neighbour and soon caught the interest of many other people of Koenigsberg as well. They pondered the question seriously, but no one could come up with an answer.

Somehow, the problem came to the attention of a Swiss mathematician by the name of Leonhard Euler, who was serving at the court of the Russian empress Catherine the Great in St. Petersburg. Euler focused his mathematical skill on the problem and eventually came up with a solution: the bridges could not be crossed in the manner posed by the problem. Perhaps the man who first raised the question was disappointed, but he may have been less unhappy had he known that, in the process of working out the problem, Euler had founded the branch of mathematics which we are now examining, topology.

In solving the Koenigsberg bridge problem, Euler didn't find it necessary to go to Koenigsberg. He remained in St. Petersburg and did what mathematicians usually do: he drew a diagram of the problem. With this diagram, the land and shore became points, and the bridges became lines connecting these points, as in Figure 18 below. Now you can work on the problem with a pencil, as Euler did. See if you can draw the figure in Figure 18*b* by starting at some point and returning to that point without retracing any line or lifting your pencil off the paper. With this drawing, Euler invented networks and discovered relationships that have been very valuable in topology.

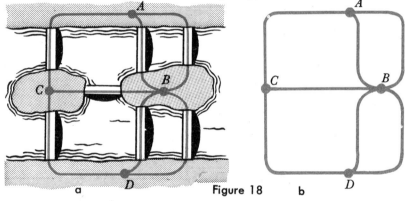

Figure 18

The diagram of the Koenigsberg bridge problem is called a *network*. The points where the lines cross are called *vertices*, and the lines representing bridges are called *arcs*. A network is *traversed* or *traced* by passing through all the arcs exactly once. You may pass through the vertices any number of times. In the network of the Koenigsberg bridges, the vertices are *A*, *B*, *C*, and *D*. The number of arcs to vertex *A* is 3, so the vertex at *A* is called an *odd vertex*. In the same way, *B* is an odd vertex, since 5 arcs go to this vertex. Euler discovered that there must be a certain number of odd vertices in any network if you are to traverse it in one journey without retracing any arcs. Euler also discovered other important laws for traversing networks. Perhaps you can discover the same ones by trying the exercises below. Copy the geometrical figures. Then study the vertices and traverse the networks to see if you can discover the relationships between vertices of closed networks, as Euler did.

EXERCISE SET 3
Network Traversing Experiment

For each network, tabulate the number of even vertices and the number of odd vertices, and then see if the network can be traversed. Copy and complete the table that follows the illustrations

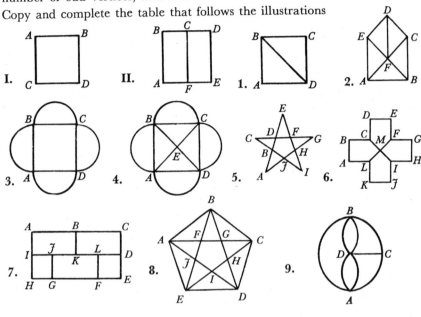

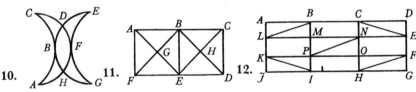

Network	Even Vertices	Odd Vertices	Can it be traversed?
I.	4	0	Yes
II.	4	2	Yes
1.			
2.			
3.			
4.			
5.			

Network	Even Vertices	Odd Vertices	Can it be traversed?
6.			
7.			
8.			
9.			
10.			
11.			
12.			

Euler's Discoveries About Networks

Many of the problems of topology are related to networks. Study the networks in Exercise Set 3 to find the answers to these questions about the relations of vertices and arcs:

1. Where does an arc always begin or end?
2. If two arcs meet, what is true about their vertices?
3. Are all parts of the network connected by arcs?
4. Can a network be traversed in one journey if it has only 2 odd vertices?
5. Can a network be traversed in one journey if it has more than 2 odd vertices?
6. Can a network be traversed in one journey if it has only odd vertices?
7. Can a network be traversed in one journey if it has only 2 even vertices?
8. Can a network be traversed in one journey if it has more than 2 even vertices?
9. Can a network be traversed in one journey if it has all even vertices?

By finding the answers to questions like these, Euler made four general discoveries about networks. First, he showed that the number of odd vertices in a network is always even if it is to be traversed in one journey. Try to traverse a network with an odd number of odd vertices in one journey. If you succeed, you will be making mathematical history!

Next, Euler found that a network of all even vertices could be traversed in one journey. In other words, we could start from any vertex, cover the entire network, and return to the same vertex without traversing any arcs twice.

Euler's third discovery was that if a network contained 2, and only 2, odd vertices it could be traversed in one journey, but it would be impossible to return to the starting point. It would be necessary in this case to start at one odd vertex and end at the other.

Euler's last discovery was that if a network contained 4, 6, 8, or any higher even number of odd vertices it would be impossible to traverse the network in one journey. In these cases the number of journeys required would be equal to half the number of odd vertices.

Let's see how this works with the Koenigsberg bridges. This network consists of 4 odd vertices, which means that it is impossible to traverse the network in one trip. In fact, Euler's fourth discovery shows that it would take exactly two trips.

While Euler was working with the Koenigsberg bridge problem he realized that he was working with a new kind of geometry. He could see that the pattern did not depend on the size of the figure or the shape of the figure. Out of these ideas grew the branch of mathematics now called topology. The networks we have studied have *not* been concerned with length, area, angles, or shape. Instead, the important thing has been places, and how the places are connected by arcs. In geometry, we study the properties of figures that remain the same when you move a figure without changing its shape. For example, a circle has a certain radius, diameter, circumference, and area which does not change if it is moved from one place to another. When we move figures in geometry the motion is rigid; that is, we do not allow any change in shape. In topology, we can move figures and change their shape by twisting or stretching, forgetting about length or distance, angles, and arcs. In topology, we study the properties of the figure that remain the same under this distortion.

Now let us see how networks apply to the curves we have discussed earlier. The simplest network is a single arc such as *AB: A* _____ *B. A* and *B* are said to be *vertices* of this single arc. Another simple network is *A* <⸺⸺⸺> *B*, the closed curve with 2 vertices and 2 arcs. However, we may locate other points on *A B*, so that it may have many vertices, such as:

A <⸺⸺⸺> *B* Examples of complex networks are the lines
C   D
E F   G
on a basketball court, or the cities and roads on a road map.

EXERCISE SET 4
Network Problems and Puzzles

1. The three houses below, *A*, *B*, and *C*, must each connect to the water main, *W*, the gas main, *G*, and the electricity, *E*. Is it possible

18

to make these connections so that no lines cross? Draw a network to help you decide whether or not it is possible. Maybe shading the drawing, as we did in the Caliph's problem, will help you find the answer to this puzzle.

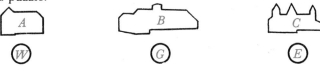

2. Is it possible to take an entire trip through a house whose floor plan is shown in the figure below and pass through each door once and only once? Try drawing a network to correspond to this figure. Let the rooms be vertices and the doors be arcs.

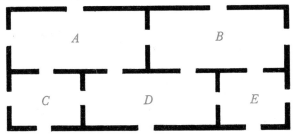

Networks, Regions, and an Important Formula

One of the questions asked about networks is the number of pieces, or regions, into which a network divides a plane surface. For example, in Figure 19a below there is only 1 region. You can go from any point in the plane to any other point in the plane without crossing the network.

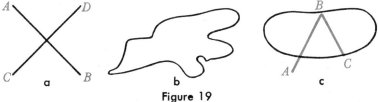

Figure 19

How many regions are there for a closed curve like the one in Figure 19b? Can you count 4 regions for the network of Figure 19c?

What relationships exist between regions, arcs, and vertices? If you study the networks in Exercise Set 5 you may be able to discover the relationship between the number of vertices (V), the number of arcs (A), and the number of regions (R) of a network.

19

EXERCISE SET 5
Networks and Regions Experiment

Copy and complete the table that follows the illustrations for each of the networks and then see whether you can state a formula relating the three variables, V, A, and R.

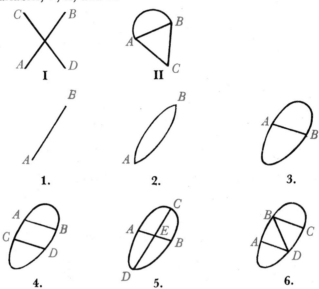

Network	V = the Number of Vertices	A = the Number of Arcs	R = the Number of Regions
I	5	4	1
II	3	4	3
1.			
2.			
3.			
4.			
5.			
6.			

Euler's Formula for Networks

If you are a mathematical wizard you would discover that
$$V - A + R = 2.$$
This is Euler's network formula and expresses one of the most important properties of networks. See if it works for the networks in Figure 20.

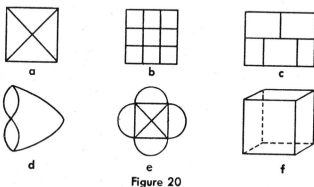

Figure 20

The Four-Colour Map Problem

One of the most famous unsolved problems in mathematics which is related to networks and regions is the four-colour map problem. Suppose we want to draw a map so that countries with a common border are coloured differently. How many different colours are needed to make this kind of map?

The drawings below illustrate some possible maps. Copy these maps and colour the countries so that countries with common borders have different colours.

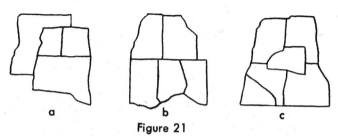

Figure 21

So far, it has been possible to colour all maps that can be thought of using only four different colours. However, it has never been proved mathematically that four colours are enough for all maps. It has been proved that five colours are sufficient to colour any

21

map, and that to colour some maps it is necessary to have at least four colours. But mathematicians are still searching for a proof to show that four colours are sufficient as well as necessary. So if you want to become famous, find a map that needs five colours or prove that four colours are sufficient.

1. Perform these exercises with a map of England.
   a. Draw a network of six counties in your region.
   b. What is the smallest number of counties that you can pass through in travelling from Cornwall to Northumberland?
   c. How many different colours are needed to colour the map of part *a* so that all counties in that region are coloured differently?
   d. What county in England borders on the greatest number of other counties, when "border on" means a common border which is more than a point?

2. Copy this map. Colour it with four colours so that no areas with common borders have the same colour.

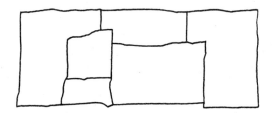

3. Draw a map with ten regions that can be coloured with three colours, no two bordering regions having the same colour.

4. Divide a circle into regions with lines so that no three lines go through the same point. What is the largest number of regions formed for each number of lines? Copy and fill in this table.

No. of Lines	No. of Regions
1	
2	
3	
4	
5	

How do the differences in number of regions compare for each cut? How many regions would you predict for six lines?

A Topological Look at Our Three-Dimensional World

Classifying Topological Figures

In our space age, of course, we should consider how topology applies to three-dimensional objects, such as spheres, cubes, and doughnut-shaped objects that occupy space.

In topology, a sphere is something like a circle. It divides space into one inside region and one outside region. A cube or a pyramid does the same. To get from a point inside these figures to the outside, the path or line crosses the surface of the object in one point. Again we assume there is no hole in the surface of the object, just as we say there is no hole in a line. This means a surface is continuous. Any closed surface which divides space into two regions, an inside and an outside, is a *simple closed surface*. So a sphere, a cube, and a pyramid are simple closed surfaces. Any simple closed surface like a cube or a pyramid can be changed to a sphere by distortion.

What is the difference between a simple closed curve and a ring or between a sphere and a doughnut? Topology says it is how the lines or surfaces are connected.

And topology tells us how to change or transform one figure or object into a different figure or object. For example, consider a ring on a flat surface, as in Figure 22.

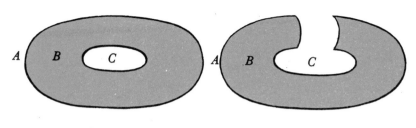

Figure 22   Figure 23

This ring figure is not a simple closed curve. It divides the sheet into three regions, *A*, *B*, and *C*. But if we cut the ring once, as in Figure 23, it becomes a simple closed curve. *A* and *C* are now both on the outside.

Topology classifies objects or figures by finding out how many cuts are needed to simplify the figure or surface. A ring like the one above is classified as a *singly* connected surface because it takes one cut to transform it to a simple closed curve. Be sure to notice that the words *singly* and *simple* mean different things in classifying figures.

In three dimensions, topology classifies an object according to the number of cuts necessary to change it to a simple closed surface like the sphere. For example, the doughnut is somewhat like the ring we described above. If we cut across a doughnut once, as shown in Figure 24, it becomes a simple closed surface that can be distorted into a sphere. Note that a single cross-cut of a simple closed surface would produce two pieces. Thus the result produced by a single cut is the primary topological distinction between a doughnut and a sphere. We say that the doughnut and the sphere differ in "connectivity."

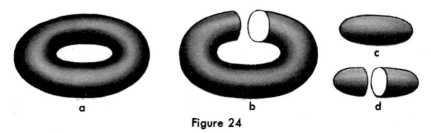

Figure 24

What about the hole in a doughnut? Is the hole in a doughnut inside or outside? In topology, we say the hole is outside, not inside. Actually, the hole in the doughnut has only a small part in topological classification definitions.

Next let's look at the edges of topological figures. A sheet of paper or a round card is said to have two surfaces and one edge. An inner tube has two surfaces but no edge. An open cylinder has two edges and two surfaces. One way to classify objects is to count the cross-cuts that can be made on a surface without dividing it into more than one piece. A cross-cut may be thought of as a cut with a pair of scissors that begins and ends on an edge.

If we make a cut from one edge of a square sheet of paper to another, we see that we divide it into two distinct parts. If we do this with a cardboard tube, we reduce it to a surface equivalent to a square. Of course, if we cut the cylinder by a line parallel to both of its edges, we get two cylinders. The square is said to be a simple surface; the cylinder, a *singly connected surface*. A punctured sphere (balloon) could be stretched and flattened into a sheet if the hole would stretch enough. So a sphere is also a singly connected surface.

Each of the three-dimensional objects in Figure 25 is *triply connected* because two cuts are needed for each to be changed to a simple closed surface, and then a third cut or puncture is needed to change the closed surface to a simple plane curve.

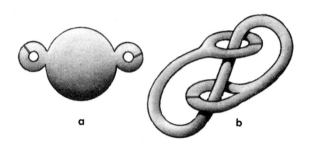

a   b

Figure 25

EXERCISE SET 7
Three-Dimensional Surfaces

1. How many cuts are needed to change these solids to simple closed surfaces?

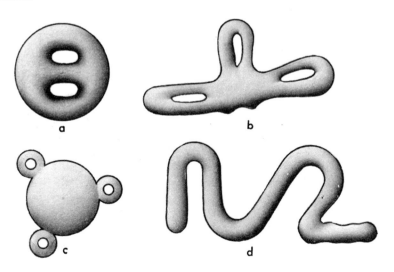

a   b

c   d

2. Classify these surfaces as singly, doubly, or triply connected surfaces or as simple surfaces.

    a. a football

    b. a garden hose

    c. a coat

    d. a long-sleeved pullover

    e. an inner tube

    f. a paper plate

    g. a paper cup with no handles

3. Because of differences in connectivity, some puzzles that cannot be solved on a simple closed surface like a plane or a sphere can be solved on a more complex surface like a torus (the technical name for a doughnut-like surface).

You should have found it impossible to do Problem 1 of Exercise Set 4 in one plane. See if you can solve this problem on a doughnut.

A Famous Mathematician's Unusual Bottle

A three-dimensional object similar to a one-sided Moebius strip is the Klein bottle, invented in 1882 by the great German mathematician, Felix Klein. The easiest way to visualize this bottle is to imagine that an inner tube is cut and straightened out like a cylinder. One end is then stretched out to make a base and the other end narrowed like the neck of a bottle. Next, the

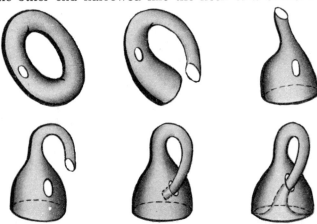

Figure 26

narrow end is twisted over and thrust through the valve-stem hole in the side of the tube. Finally, this end is stretched out and joined with the open end at the base. This may be called a "punctured" Klein bottle, the hole in the tube being the puncture in the bottle. In topology, we usually suppose that no hole actually exists, so that the one-sided surface passes through itself. This, of course, is actually impossible to do with an inner tube, but in topology we make free use of such queer possibilities. A Klein bottle may be thought of as a pair of Moebius bands with the edges glued together.

These properties of Moebius bands and Klein bottles have been summarized in a pair of limericks:

A mathematician confided
That a Moebius band is one-sided.
  And you'll get quite a laugh
  If you cut one in half,
For it stays in one piece when
  divided.

A mathematician named Klein
Thought the Moebius band was
  divine.
  Said he, "If you glue
  The edges of two,
You'll get a weird bottle like
  mine."

Euler's Formula Looks at the Third Dimension

Euler's network formula, $V - A + R = 2$, can be applied to certain three-dimensional figures called *polyhedra*. A polyhedron is a solid made up of parts of plane surfaces called *faces* of the polyhedron. A brick is one example of a polyhedron. In a *regular polyhedron*, such as a cube, the faces are geometrical figures with all sides and all angles equal, all faces have the same shape and size (are congruent), and the angles at which the faces meet can be made to coincide.

There are five and only five regular polyhedra. We have already mentioned the cube as one example of a regular polyhedron. A polyhedron with six faces is called a *hexahedron*. Since a cube is a regular polyhedron with six faces, it is called a *regular* hexahedron. The other polyhedra that can be regular are those with four faces *(tetrahedron)*, eight faces *(octahedron)*, twelve faces *(dodecahedron)*, and twenty faces *(icosahedron)*. The regular polyhedra are pictured in Figure 27. Find models of these polyhedra. You can make models yourself out of cardboard, using the patterns of Figure 28.

When applying Euler's formula to polyhedra, we often change the symbol A to E to represent the number of edges of the polyhedron, and change R to F to represent the number of faces. Do you see that a polyhedron is really a three-dimensional network?

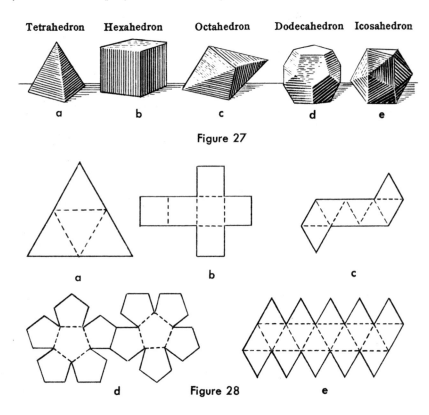

Tetrahedron   Hexahedron   Octahedron   Dodecahedron Icosahedron

a   b   c   d   e

Figure 27

a   b   c

d   Figure 28   e

EXERCISE SET 8
Polyhedra and Euler's Formula

Copy this table and fill in the blanks.

Name	Number of Faces (F)	Number of Edges (E)	Number of Vertices (V)	V+F	E+2
1. Tetrahedron					
2. Hexahedron					
3. Octahedron					
4. Dodecahedron					
5. Icosahedron					

Tricks and Fun
with Topology

Topology is such a curious kind of mathematics that it can very easily be used to mystify people who are not acquainted with it. We saw one example of this with the Moebius strip. There are many other odd and unusual effects that can be achieved through various applications of topology, and you may want to present these at parties and other gatherings for the delight and/or mystification of your friends. Also, topology has many interesting problems and puzzles that are fun to try to solve at gatherings. Some of these are given in the following pages. Why not try them? If you need help, you will find the solutions at the back of this book.

Knots and Topology

One application of topology is the study of knots in a string. If a knot is loosely tied, it is possible to work it along the string toward the end of the string. Suppose we tie two knots in a string, as in Figure 29.

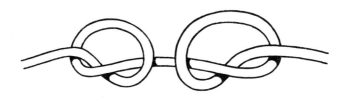

Figure 29

Now work the knots toward each other. These knots are the opposite of each other. Yet they will not untie each other when brought together. Instead, one passes through the other and out the other side, leaving both knots unchanged. Experiments show that this is always true with these knots, but no one has been able to prove it.

A false knot known as the Chefalo Knot is an example of knots which are used by magicians. It begins as a square knot as in

Figure 30*a*. Then one end is woven in and out as shown in Figure 30*b* by arrows. When the ends are pulled, the knot disappears.

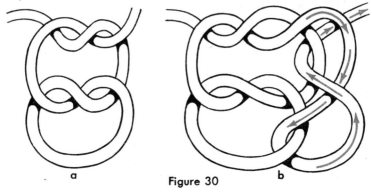

a   **Figure 30**   b

Buttonholing a Friend

Tie a loop of string to a pencil or a short stick. Be sure the loop is shorter than the pencil. Attach the pencil to the buttonhole of a friend's jacket without untying the loop, as shown in Figure 31*b*. Pull the loop tight, as shown in Figure 31*c*. Ask your friend to remove the pencil without untying or cutting the loop (or his buttonhole!). If he doesn't see you put it on, he will have a hard time removing it.

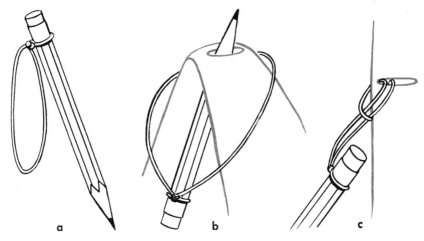

a   b   c

Figure 31

A variation of this puzzle is to loop a string through a pair of scissors and then tie the ends of the string to a large button, as shown in Figure 32. The button must be larger than the opening in the handle of the scissors. The problem is to remove the button from the pair of scissors without untying or cutting the string.

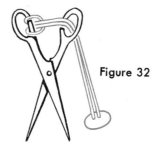

Figure 32

Undressing on the Beach

The object of this trick is to remove your waistcoat without removing your coat. Put on a waistcoat and a coat. If the waistcoat is large, the trick is easier to perform. The coat may be unbuttoned, but you are not permitted to let your arms slip out of your coat sleeves.

The Ring Puzzle

The three rings pictured below have a strange topological relation. Remove any one ring, and the other two will be found to be free, too. Thus, no two rings are joined, but the three put together are.

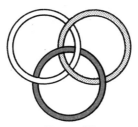

Figure 33

Stringing Along

Tie a piece of string to each of your wrists. Tie a second piece of string to each of the wrists of a partner in such a way that the second string loops the first. The object of this trick is to separate yourself from your partner without cutting the string, untying the knots, or taking the string off your wrists. This can be done!

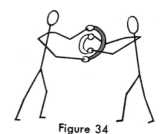

Figure 34

Buttons and Beads

To make this puzzle you need cardboard, string, two buttons,

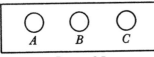

Figure 35

and two beads. Cut a rectangular piece of cardboard about 1 inch by 6 inches. Cut three small, evenly spaced holes, as in Figure 35.

String two large beads on the string. Thread one end of the string through hole *A* and attach a button larger than the hole. In the same direction, thread the other end of the string through hole *C* and attach a button as in Figure 36*a*.

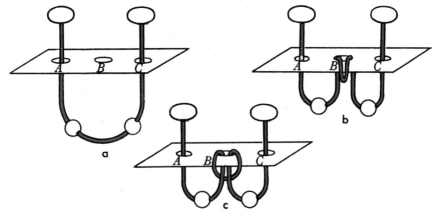

Figure 36

The string is then looped through hole *B*, as in Figure 36*b*. To loop it back under itself, as in Figure 36*c*, the loop is first threaded up in hole *A* and over the button and then likewise in hole *C*. The puzzle is now ready for someone to try to undo the loop and get the beads together.

The Swiss School Problem

Four Swiss schoolboys live at homes *A*, *B*, *C*, *D*. They go to the same school and must enter doors *A*, *B*, *C*, *D*. Boy *A* lives in

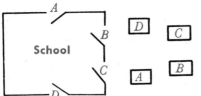

Figure 37

home *A* and goes to door *A*, *B* goes from home *B* to door *B*, and so on. How can they ski to school without their tracks crossing?

The Divided Farm

A wealthy farmer with four sons owned a three-section farm having the shape shown in Figure 38. When he died, his will said that the farm should be divided so that each son got one-fourth

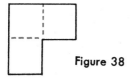

Figure 38

of his farm. He also stated that each farm must have the same shape as the original farm. How was the farm divided?

Pennies on the Square

Draw a 6-by-6 square chess board. Place six pennies on this board so that no penny is in line with another penny horizontally, vertically, or diagonally. No square may have more than one penny.

The Road Sweeper's Route

A road sweeper must sweep each of the streets shown in Figure 39. To cover the area, he must pass some blocks twice. How should he plan his route so that he can cover it by traversing the least number of blocks possible? He may start at any corner.

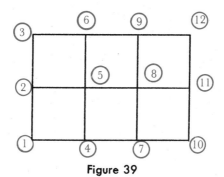

Figure 39

The Paper and String Puzzle

Take a piece of stiff paper and cut it so it measures 6 inches long by 3 inches wide. Now cut two parallel slits half an inch apart in the centre of the paper, as shown in Figure 40. Each slit is 3 inches long. Half an inch above the slits, cut a circular hole having a diameter of ¾ inch.

Pass a piece of string about 12 inches long behind the slits and then down through the hole, as shown in the drawing, and tie a large button to each end of the string. Be sure that each of the buttons is too large to pass through the ¾-inch hole in the paper.

Now ask one of your friends to remove the string and buttons from the paper without tearing the paper or taking off either of the buttons. There is little chance of his succeeding unless you show him how.

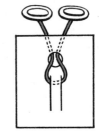

Figure 40

The Paper Boot Puzzle

The boot puzzle consists of three pieces, all of which are cut out of stiff paper. One piece is shaped like a pair of boots joined together at the top, as in Figure 41a. The remaining pieces are shaped as shown in Figure 41b and c.

To assemble the puzzle, fold the large rectangular piece as in Figure 41b and slip the smaller piece over one of its arms, as in Figure 41d. Then hang the boots over part of the same arm, as in Figure 41e. Pull the small piece to the right and over the end of the arm at A. Then unfold the large piece, and the puzzle will be assembled as in Figure 41f.

The problem is to remove the boots without tearing the paper.

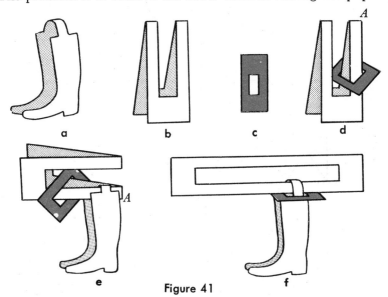

Figure 41

34

Take this test to see how much you remember about the ideas you have come across in this book.

1. Which figure in each set of four does not belong with the rest?

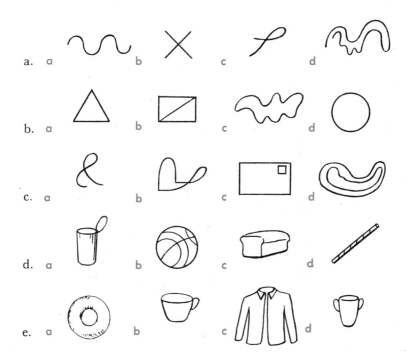

a. a   b   c   d

b. a   b   c   d

c. a   b   c   d

d. a   b   c   d

e. a   b   c   d

2. Which of the following networks can be traversed in one journey?

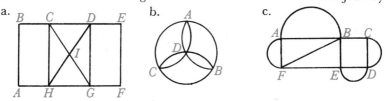

a.   b.   c.

3. Which of the following are invariant under a topological transformation?

    a. The number of regions in the figure.

    b. The value of $(V+R-A)$ in a network.

    c. The length of a line.

d. Continuity.

e. The shape of the figure.

4. What is the minimum number of trips needed to trace this network?

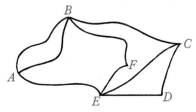

5. Name all vertices where you can start to trace the above network in the minimum number of trips.

6. The following diagram shows a fleet of boats which are tied up near a dock. The boats are connected by gangplanks as indicated. Show by use of a network whether or not it is possible to make one trip and cross all of the gangplanks only once. If not, what is the minimum number of trips?

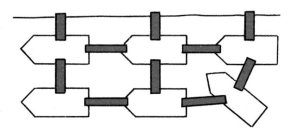

7. Show that Euler's formula for vertices, arcs, and regions is satisfied for each of the following figures.

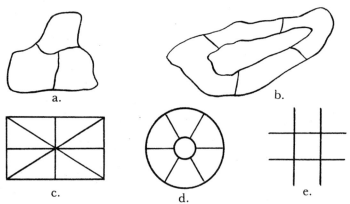

Demonstration Models for Topology

In addition to the models, drawings, and tricks described in this book, there are other models that will demonstrate the ideas of topology. These will enliven and add interest to a science exhibition. Here are some suggested models.

1. Make drawings of a geometrical figure on several rubber sheets. Show how the figure changes when the sheets are stretched in various ways.

2. Cut 12 lengths of drinking straws each about 2 inches long. Thread elastic thread through these straws to form a cube. Show how this cube can be distorted or flattened or changed into a network.

3. Draw a network or map on several balloons. Show how this network or map remains equivalent with the balloons blown up to different sizes.

4. Stretch a rubber sheet or balloon over a geometrical solid. Show how the geometrical solid and a sphere have the same characteristics.

5. Use modelling clay to form models of objects to show different types of topological surfaces.

6. Make a Klein bottle out of rubber or knit one out of yarn.

7. Make large Moebius strips out of adding machine tape. Cut in different ways to show the many possible results.

8. Make diagrams of complex maps to demonstrate the four-colour problem.

We have presented some of the basic concepts and interesting applications of topology. But this field of study is not concerned only with tricks, puzzles, and fascinating problems. A technical study of topology is often a part of advanced work in mathematics, and involves many ideas that are far beyond the scope of this book. These concepts are developed in much the same way that theorems are developed in school geometry. Mathematicians are applying topological concepts to many practical problems, and topology is becoming a valuable tool in our complex space age.

For Further Reading

COURANT, RICHARD, and ROBBINS, HERBERT, 'Topology', in James Newman's *The World of Mathematics*, Vol. I, pp. 581–599, Allen & Unwin, 1960.

CUNDY, H. M., and ROLLETT, A. P., *Mathematical Models*, O.U.P., 1961.

EULER, LEONHARD, 'The Seven Bridges of Koenigsberg', in James Newman's *The World of Mathematics*, Vol. I, pp. 573-580, Allen & Unwin, 1960.

GAMOW, GEORGE, *One, Two, Three, Infinity*, Macmillan, 1947.

GOODSTEIN, L., *Fundamental Concepts of Mathematics*, Pergamon Press, 1962.

KASNER, EDWARD, and NEWMAN, JAMES, *Mathematics and the Imagination*, Bell, 1949.

Solutions to the Exercises

EXERCISE SET 1

1. *a, c*   2. *a, b*   3. *a*—2; *b*—3; *c*—0; *d*—5

EXERCISE SET 2

Number of half-twists	Number of sides and edges	Results of cut
0	2	2 separate loops
1	1	1 loop, 2 twists
1	1	2 loops interlocked
2	2	2 loops interlocked
2	2	2 loops interlocked
3	1	1 loop, 1 knot
3	1	2 loops interlocked, 1 knot

EXERCISE SET 3

Figure	Even Vertices	Odd Vertices	Traversed
1.	2	2	Yes
2.	0	6	No
3.	4	0	Yes
4.	1	4	No
5.	10	0	Yes
6.	9	4	No
7.	4	8	No
8.	10	0	Yes
9.	2	2	Yes
10.	8	0	Yes
11.	2	6	No
12.	14	2	Yes

EXERCISE SET 4

1. Impossible   2. Impossible

EXERCISE SET 5

	V	A	R
1.	2	1	1
2.	2	2	2
3.	2	3	3
4.	4	6	4
5.	5	8	5
6.	4	7	5

EXERCISE SET 6

1. *b.* 8   *c.* 4   *d.* Northamptonshire
2. Many arrangements of colour are possible.
4. No. of regions: 2, 4, 7, 11, 16
   Differences: 2, 3, 4, 5
   With six lines: 22 regions

EXERCISE SET 7

1. *a*—2; *b*—3; *c*—3; *d*—0
2. *a.* singly; *b.* singly; *c.* doubly; *d.* triply; *e.* doubly; *f.* simple; *g.* simple

EXERCISE SET 8

	F	E	V	V+F	E+2
1.	4	6	4	8	8
2.	6	12	8	14	14
3.	8	12	6	14	14
4.	12	30	20	32	32
5.	20	30	12	32	32

EXERCISE SET 9

1. a.   d.
   b.
   e.
   c.

2. a, b, c
3. a, b, c
4. One
5. Any odd vertex
6. Two
7.

V	A	R
4	6	4
8	12	6
9	16	9
12	18	8
12	12	2

PUZZLE SOLUTIONS

Page 31. Undressing on the Beach

You can remove the waistcoat by putting your left hand and arm through the left armhole. Then bring the entire coat and the right arm through this armhole of the waistcoat. Finally, stuff the waistcoat down the right coat sleeve and it will be off.

Page 31. Stringing Along

Loop your string under the wrist loop of your partner. Pull your loop over his hand and you will be free.

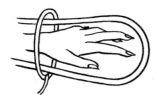

Page 32. Buttons and Beads

As in "Stringing Along," loop the centre strings through the end holes and over the buttons.

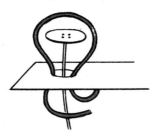

Page 32. The Swiss School Problem

Go around the houses.

Page 33. The Divided Farm

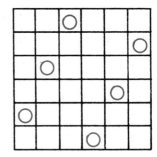

Page 33. Pennies on the Square

Page 33. The Road Sweeper's Route

Begin at any odd vertex. You will need to retrace three blocks.

Page 33. Paper and String Puzzle

Curve the paper as shown below and push the strip between the two slits through the hole from back to front. Either one of the buttons can then be passed through the loop formed by the centre strip, and the string can easily be removed.

Page 34. The Paper Boot Puzzle

The boots can be removed by reversing the steps described. First refold the large piece of paper. Then slide the small piece back around point *A* and into position as shown in Figure 41*d*. The boots can then be lifted from the arm over which they are suspended.